to: _____

from: _____

date: _____

Mother's Moments

Published by Garborg's Heart 'n Home, Inc.
P.O. Box 20132
Bloomington, MN 55420

SPCN 5-5044-0091-0

January 1

Wake up! Enjoy today!
God made it perfect in every way.
Find the good! Avoid the bad!
Teach your child to rejoice and be glad.

December 31

He will make you confident in your decisions,
He will be right by your side.
He will give you love, patience, and wisdom,
You've found the "source", now let *Him* guide!

Treat your children as God's gift,
Then you'll feel His spiritual lift.

January 2

By praying this today,
Be assured He's in your life
Helping you each moment,
Especially those filled with strife.

So use Him, rely on Him,
Talk to Him every day.
Thank Him, cry to Him,
He'll show you the way.

...continued

December 30

January 3

"Please forgive me,"
Leaves you vulnerable, that's true,
But said to your child,
Opens a relationship that's new.

"I thank you too, Lord,
    for dying for my sin.
I receive you as my Savior.
    Please, Lord, do come in!

Make me the daughter,
Wife, and mother you have
    in mind.

You're in control now,
You're the "source"
I've needed to find."

...continued

December 29

I wish I could capture this feeling
And box it up real tight.
Then store it on the shelf
For when my arms are empty
    at night.

Then some day when I'm alone
    and feel
My child doesn't need me as much,
I could take down my special box
And warm memories I'd hug
    and touch.

January 4

Say, "Lord, I need your help
    to raise your precious gift.
I can't do it alone, I need
    your spiritual lift.

Lord, take control of the good
    days and the bad;
I give back to you Lord, the power
    I thought I had."
                    ...continued

December 28

Two socks per person are worn
    each day,
But after the wash, one's
    run away.

January 5

It's an awesome responsibility,
But you don't have to feel alone.
There's a source of strength
   and direction
To use as your cornerstone.

It's very simple to receive
And doesn't take much time.
Just mean it from your heart
And it's yours for a lifetime.

...continued

December 27

Rejoice in the Lord always. I will say it again: Rejoice!

Philippians 4:4

January 6

December 26

Your child is the future; he could change this place.
He's watching and learning from the problems you face.
He mimics what you do, he repeats what you say;
You're the most important influence on how he
    grows each day.

...continued

January 7

As I tiptoe into your bedroom each night
To pull up the covers and tuck you in tight,
I linger longer just watching you sleep,
And think of our day and the memories I'll keep.

December 25

For to you is born this day in the city of David a Savior, who is Christ the Lord.

Luke 2:11 RSV

January 8

Use me, show me the way,
To be the best mom I can be today.
I am yours, You made me,
Please use me today!

You are my Savior, my Lord, and the Way,
You died for my sins, I'm free today!
I am yours, You made me,
So use me today!

December 24

JESUS, TOMORROW'S YOUR BIRTHDAY!!

We've made you a cake,
Put a candle on it, too.
Before we open presents
We'll sing, "Happy Birthday to you!"

January 9

If children are the ones who take the baths,
   why are moms the ones who get soaking wet?

THE FIRST CHRISTMAS

No tinsel, no carols, or even snow.
In the little town of Bethlehem so long ago.

No hotel, no home, no room at all,
Just the warmth of a manger in a lowly stall.

God gave us this gift! God gave us His Son!
Now let there be peace and love to everyone.

January 10

Dependable, fun, trustworthy, too,
Loving, kind, plays peek-a-boo.
Not too old or too young; it's hard to find
The perfect babysitter you have in mind.

December 22

Read me more Mommy...
About that first Christmas day
When Jesus was born and slept
    on the hay.

Read me more Mommy...
Did He cry? Was He cold?
Why is it the greatest story
    ever told?

Read me more Mommy...
About the three Wisemen's gifts.
Do you think He would like my
    big hug and kiss?

January 11

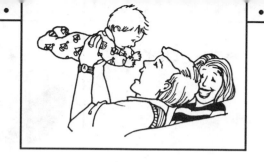

Often God's biggest gifts to us
    come in the littlest of packages...our children.

Small children hear our words of love and concern
much more readily when our eyes meet at the same level.

Children are a gift from God; they are his reward.

Psalm 127:3 TLB

January 12

December 20

My children sing in the front row,
"Jesus loves me this I know."
The song is old, but the words are true;
Help them believe and trust in You.

I look in the mirror and what
    do I see,
But little wrinkles creeping
    up on me!
They'd appear if I was a mom
    or not,
But let them be from laughter and
    merry thoughts.

January 13

December 19

The sparkle in my child's eyes
Of wonder and delight
Shines brighter than any Christmas lights
Glowing in the night.

January 14

Often when a child asks for something more,
He wants you to say "no" and close the door.
He knows what's right and what you say is best;
Don't spoil him, this is only a test.

December 18

The Lord himself goes before you and will be
with you; he will never leave you nor forsake you.
Do not be afraid; do not be discouraged.

Deuteronomy 31:8

Many times I wish I had more
    hands to help me through
    the day.
Evening is the toughest—
    making dinner, helping with
    homework, a toddler who
    wants to play.

Some call it crazy or "arsenic hour."
    I feel it's my own personal test.
Now's the time to give it to Him,
    ask His guidance to do my best.

January 15

December 17

How can I feel lonely
When there are so many people around?
How can I feel lonely
When there's never a quiet sound?

But I do feel lonely,
My heart aches deep inside.
I need You, don't leave me...
Please be at my side.

January 16

We like to walk in the cold, crisp air,
Hearing the snow crunch beneath our feet.
We talk, watching white clouds from our mouths
Then walk again; the silence is so sweet.

A patch of untouched snow beckons us
To stop, and just play a short while.
We plop down, making angels in the snow
Bringing us joy and a smile.

December 16

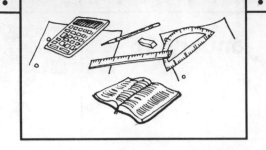

Math and science are good for my child to know;
I'm sure facts and figures will help his mind grow,
But if taught alone without learning rules of the heart—
Forgiveness and love—his teaching has only been in part.

A Blessing

The peace of God, which transcends all understanding, will guard your hearts and your minds in Christ Jesus.

Philippians 4:7

January 17

December 15

Lord, help me keep
My priorities straight.
First comes You,
All else can wait.

January 18

Everyone was created equal yet unique by God.
We need to teach our children by our example
how to see others through His eyes.

No one spilled the milk today,
Nobody cried when they didn't
    get their way,
No one fought for the same toy,
Nobody got hit by the bully boy.

Now that I think of it,
I had a great day—
By counting my blessings
In this strange way.

December 14

January 19

My child did what she was asked the very first time,
I gave her a gold star instead of candy or a dime.
One minute per star is the reward, you see,
For time alone with Dad or time with me.

What better way to start a
	school day
Than with a prayer and a kiss
Before they're on their way.

December 13

January 20

"Mom likes you best!"
I hear my older child say.
Is there truth in those words?
Do I speak or act that way?

I can love each child differently,
I can appreciate each unique gift;
But I must affirm and show love equally
To give each one's self-esteem a lift.

A Blessing

May our Lord Jesus Christ himself and God our Father, who loved us and by his grace gave us eternal encouragement and good hope, encourage your hearts and strengthen you in every good deed and word.

2 Thessalonians 2:16,17

December 12

January 21

Carpool moms have a captive audience...
   Use this unique opportunity to
      listen, laugh, sing, and teach.

Though I'm busy at work
And can't watch you play,
Thoughts of you make me smile;
I giggled out loud one day.

During my lunch hour I eat,
Then rush to the store.
Near the clothes and toys
I think of you that much more.

December 11

January 22

Let the word of Christ dwell in you richly as you teach and admonish one another with all wisdom, and as you sing psalms, hymns and spiritual songs with gratitude in your hearts to God.

Colossians 3:16

December 10

My grandchildren are my gift and joy,
We read, walk, cook, and play with toys.
But when I need to get off my feet,
Handing them back to mom is oh, so sweet.

My daughter wakes a little
   grouchy today.
No smiles or giggles, doesn't
   want to play.

I know what she needs, just takes
   a little time
To give hugs and kisses to this
   child of mine.

January 23

December 9

I think about the perfect gifts
That I could give away...
Like love, hugs, a smile,
And more time to listen and play.

January 24

When children play together well,
Don't be silent, afraid to break the spell.
Tell them how you like their play;
It brings you joy when they act that way.

My primary purpose at Christmas
    time is *not*
    to buy presents, decorate the
    house, and write cards.

My purpose and responsibility
    is to make sure
    my child knows whose birthday
    we are celebrating, and why.

December 8

Jesus, you are an example;
    you showed us how to live.
To love one another and
    unselfishly to give.

Now help me be an example
    to my child every day,
Loving unconditionally in all
    I do and say.

January 25

December 7

When I'm in a rush to get out the door,
My child wants to play with one toy more.
I say, "Hurry!" Then she goes so slow.
Yet it's not really on purpose, that I know.

I need to get up earlier and plan better each day,
So there's time for surprises that get in my way.
I need to give notice before I say, "Go",
Then she'll be more ready with smiles aglow.

Above all, love each other deeply, because love covers over a multitude of sins.

1 Peter 4:8

January 26

December 6

Look through Jesus' eyes at your girl or boy.
Feel His love, compassion, forgiveness, and joy.

January 27

We prayed a long time
Asking God for you.
We shared our dreams
And cried to Him, too.

He listened and answered
Our prayerful plea,
And that's when He gave you
To your dad and me!

December 5

Am I more interested in completing my lists today
Than being kind and loving in the things I do and say?

January 28

"Mom, it's too cold. It's been snowing all day!
Please don't make me go to school today."
But when school is closed, and it's colder still...
Guess who's outside sledding down the hill?

December 4

To keep my home centered only on You,
I need to pray daily asking You what to do.

January 29

If there is one thing your child should know,
It's that your love is with him wherever he may go.
You may not like what he may say or do,
But let love be constant and forgiving from you.

December 3

Eyelash kisses on the cheek of a child
Land softly as snowflakes on a tree in the wild.

January 30

God can wash all your cares away,
Just ask Him in and ask Him to stay.
He'll give you strength, renew your joy,
And you'll have more patience for your girl or boy.

Starting a new Christmas tradition
   this year is easy.
Remembering to do it again next
   year is what's hard.

December 2

Shopping in a new grocery store is like driving in a new town without a map...confusing, time-consuming, seeing things you've never seen before.

Make it an adventure to explore!

January 31

December 1

Something curious is happening, I'd like to know
   the reason.
Strangers stop to pat me as if tummies are "open season."

Now don't get me wrong, I love hugs and kisses.
I'm just trying to figure out exactly what *this* is.

It sort of tickles, but seems odd and strange to me...
People who would pass me by, now want to touch and see.

February 1

In our hurry to see a childhood stage go,
We might miss unexpected joys we'd treasure so.

Teach your children to first obey,
Then let them ask the why's
    to what you say.

For keeping them safe is your
    first concern;
Now they're too young to decide
    and discern.

November 30

Is it spring or more winter still?
More icicles or daffodils?
Does it matter anyway?
Just make the most of God's
    new day!

February 2

November 29

Come, my children, listen to me; I will teach you the fear of the Lord.

Psalm 34:11

February 3

My everyday dishes don't cost that much.
No special treatment, no place in the hutch.
I have a purpose, I have a good plan,
This way my kids can lend a helping hand.

November 28

I might not be able to play games with you,
Like running, jumping, and hopscotch, too.
But give me a board game and I'll show you my stuff;
Beating me at that will be sort of tough.

I might not be able to pick you up
Or chase you on all fours like a frisky pup.
But you can sit on my lap as I read and sing
Stories about Jesus, our Savior and King.

February 4

Why do I worry about all that might be?
I should give it to You, Lord, only You can see.
Please care for him, protect him from the bad out there;
He's Your child before mine, it's Your burden to bear.
I pray for Your peace and a settled mind,
Take control of our child, he's one of a kind.

Usually we can overlook our
   children's faults.
Why can't we do the same for
   our husband's?

November 27

February 5

Do not be anxious about anything, but in everything,
by prayer and petition, with thanksgiving,
present your requests to God.

Philippians 4:6

November 26

And whatever you do, whether in word or deed, do it all in the name of the Lord Jesus, giving thanks to God the Father through him.

Colossians 3:17

February 6

Playing tennis off the wall,
Dribbling balls down the hall,
Wrestling with Dad on the floor,
Life with boys isn't a bore.

November 25

As children pass from child to adult,
The problems of teen years seem our fault.
Release your child to God above,
Then feel His direction and His love.

February 7

Nurse you,
rock you,
hug you,
hold you.

Teach you,
train you,
love you,
let you...go.

November 24

When you kneel by her bed
To thank God for the day,
But your daughter's wound up
From a busy day at play;

Turn around and hug her,
Cuddle and feel her calm,
Start again in a different way;
Say a prayer and sing a psalm.

February 8

When ice crystals form on a cold window pane
Blocking your view of a snow-covered lane,
Don't scrape them away to see the outside,
Stop and take time to see the beauty inside.

A child's spirit is like a crystal, delicate and fine,
Growing slowly in all directions and not a straight line.
Anger's heat may melt it, hurtful words scrape it away.
Appreciate your child's inside, not just his outside today.

November 23

Family traditions are important,
It's the string in family ties.
Start a new family tradition—
Let the kids make pumpkin pies.

February 9

It's Valentine's week and if your child asks you,
"What is love? How will I know when it's true?"
I found "love" defined in my favorite Book,
And after reading that, there's no place else to look.

...continued

November 22

I try to teach my child what's right and wrong
In my deeds, my words, and even in song.
But in newspapers, music, TV, and the rest,
It's said, "It might be wrong, but it *is* the best."
Give my child strength to do what's right in Your eyes,
Help him say "no" to wrong and be godly wise.

February 10

"Love is patient and kind,
No jealousy or envy should I feel,
Never boastful or proud,
Just be unselfish and 'real'."

...continued

November 21

Family night...What should we do?
Family night...Try something new.
Family night...No phone to ring.
Family night...A new song to sing.
Family night...Together having fun,
Ending with praises for God's Son.

"Love is not haughty,
Nor demanding of its own way,
It's not irritable or touchy,
To things you may say."

...continued

February 11

Like my child, I'm learning
    to say "no"
To committees and functions
    and places to go.

Time is precious, children
    grow so fast.
I want to savor each moment
    and make it last.

November 20

February 12

"Love does not hold grudges,
And won't notice when you do wrong.
It's not glad about injustice;
When truth wins, rejoices in song."

...continued

A Blessing

The Lord watches over you—the Lord is your shade at your right hand; the sun will not harm you by day, nor the moon by night. The Lord will keep you from all harm—he will watch over your life; the Lord will watch over your coming and going both now and forevermore.

Psalm 121:5-8

November 19

February 13

"If you love someone you will be loyal,
And believe in whatever he may do.
Expect the best of him, defend him;
Then your love will be ever-new."

1 Corinthians 13:4-7 (paraphrased)

November 18

The alarm rings—
I think about my day.
It's cold and dark,
In bed I'd rather stay.

But duty calls,
Yet it's quiet for a change;
I'll take time to pray.
My outlook He'll rearrange.

February 14

VALENTINE'S DAY

The best Valentine you can give your children
    is to show love and appreciation for their Dad.

November 17

Talking on the phone and sitting on the toilet
have one thing in common...that's when your child *must*
talk with you and it can't wait.

Being silent,
Yet knowing the truth when
    a lie is told,
Is like telling the lie yourself,
Whether you are young or old.

February 15

November 16

A call from your teacher
Telling me about what you did
Makes me feel sad and confused,
For it's something we forbid.

But first, let me hear your story;
Tell me honestly about your day.
I'll listen and try to be fair,
For I love you in every way.

A mom's hug brings smiles,
Heals hurts, and warms the heart.

February 16

The magazines say,
"Dress for Success."

For a mother of a baby, success is when her dress has no burp or nursing stains, all of its buttons, and is ironed at least ten minutes before she dashes out the door.

November 15

A child is a gift, a miracle to hold,
God's gift to us, a gift of gold.
I'll learn to protect, to guard
      and defend,
'Cause His helpless creation needs
      more than a friend.

I'll trust and have faith; He will
      teach me, I know,
How to love and train her in the
      way she should go.

February 17

Read *to* them when they're young,
Read *with* them when they're old,
And they will read forever
Without being told.

November 14

February 18

Train a child in the way he should go,
and when he is old he will not turn from it.

Proverbs 22:6

November 13

Let the peace of Christ rule in your hearts,
since as members of one body you were called
to peace. And be thankful.

Colossians 3:15

February 19

I need to do something just for me:
Take a class, make a craft, something to touch and see.
Diapering, cooking, and cleaning have their place,
But if I don't find something soon...I'll be a basket case.

I might disagree with what my
    husband might say;
I might handle it differently
    if I did it my way.

But we must support each another
    and stand strong as one,
Learning, forgiving, and growing...
    or we'll be overrun.

November 12

February 20

It's snowing hard and my friend calls from the Coast,
Sharing stories of sun and sand, not meaning to boast.
As I wipe up the puddles of snow on my floor,
Grey skies, wet jackets, I could say "NO more!"
But I listen intently, glad for the fun she's found,
For I can choose to be happy, even with snow all around.

November 11

If we spent as much time teaching our children
To communicate and to resolve conflicts with love
As we do letting them watch violent TV
Or fighting with guns and gloves,
Then we might see gentle peace
And discussions instead of wars.

But, it's the mothers of future soldiers
Who must first open these new doors.

Offer your child choices today,
What she might do or wear.
Let her see results of her choices,
So later she's not caught unaware.

February 21

November 10

Help them memorize
each side,
So eight reasons they
will know
Of when to say, "Stop," "I can't,"
"I won't," and "It's definitely *no!*"

February 22

Just add water and stir.
Tear it open and eat.
Microwave most anything
For a quick and tasty treat.

A convenience world,
Everything's instant and fast.
But faith, trust, and love take time,
If you want them to last.

November 9

UNSAFE...

To themselves
Or to others it may hurt.
Help them be aware
And on "accident alert."

continued...

February 23

I know a mom who can do it all...
Work, keep house, even play kickball.
To coin a phrase, she's "Supermom" for sure,
But why do I feel so inadequate around her?

Lord, when envy is clouding my vision to see,
Show me the talents and gifts you've given me.
Then give me the strength, courage, and love I need
To praise and encourage her, then I'll be freed.

November 8

NOT ENOUGH TIME...

Is often a real answer
To give them today.
But if the request is worthy,
Find time another day.

continued...

February 24

There are different kinds of gifts, but the same Spirit.
There are different kinds of service, but the same Lord.

1 Corinthians 12:4,5

November 7

DISHONEST...

By their actions, words,
Or silence, too.
I need to trust and believe
That everything they say is true.

continued...

February 25

I'm all dressed up,
I have so much to do,
Then the sitter calls,
she has a bad flu.
My baby cries,
so I pick her right up,
My dress gets stained
from the milk in her cup.
The doorbell rings,
I open the door,
The dog runs away,
can I take any more?
The ads on the TV say
we can do it all,
On days like this, I'd like
to give *them* a call.

November 6

INCONSIDERATE...

Of someone's feelings,
Property, or even their privacy.
Ask, "How would I feel
If someone did this to me?"

continued...

February 26

Toilet paper, like streamers, decorates the hall.
Do I grab the camera, or "time out" do I call?

November 5

ILLEGAL...

Means a definite "no"
From me and our
    country's laws.
There are no if's or maybe's,
But do explain the "because."

continued...

February 27

At bedtime when the lights are low,
My child shares what bothers him so.
I listen, give a hug, wipe away a tear,
Tell him I love him and God is near.

November 4

CAN'T AFFORD IT...

Even though all
    their friends
May own one today.
They might work and earn it,
It will be more appreciated that way.

continued...

All Scripture is God-breathed and is useful for teaching, rebuking, correcting and training in righteousness.

2 Timothy 3:16

February 28

November 3

UNHEALTHY...

To their bodies—
Maybe to their minds, too.
Their bodies are a gift
And can't be fixed with Elmer's Glue®.

continued...

February 29

An extra day...Oh Lord,
  what should I do?
How do I make it special,
  this four-year gift from You?

Do I call a lonely friend,
  or send a note or card?
Do I take time to build a tower
  or play out in the yard?

Lead me, direct me
  in Your choice for me today;
I want to make a difference
  and not throw it away.

November 2

NOT OLD ENOUGH...

To handle
   responsibility—
Whether they're two
   or a new teen
I give options and my reasons
So they understand what I mean.

continued...

March 1

Toys clutter the once clean floor.
Things used to be neat when I walked through the door.
Single days were quiet, predictable but a bore,
I'll choose the mess...let's play some more.

There comes a time
When every mom has to say "no,"
To protect and direct her children
In the way they should go.

Eight sides of a stop sign
Are a good tool to teach
The why's and when's to say "no;"
Their conscience to reach.

continued....

November 1

March 2

By tickling tiny toes,
Her laughter lightly lifts
The daily dishes drudgery,
She's God's gracious gift.

October 31

A gentle answer turns away wrath,
but a harsh word stirs up anger.

Proverbs 15:1

Hair combed, shoes tied,
Everyone looks so neat.
Beds made, dishes washed,
I did it! What a feat!

Turn my back, grab my purse,
Crash! Splat! What is that I hear?
Orange juice splattered
    everywhere,
Lord, give me patience to
    persevere.

March 3

October 30

Like a guardrail on a mountain road
Lessens a driver's fears,
Fair rules and limits set with love
Often prevent needless tears.

March 4

When your child does something 'wrong',
Never say, "bad boy," for that's too strong.
Say, "I love you, and what you *did* was bad,
But God made you, and for that I'm glad!"

October 29

My busy toddler pulled down my purse today;
The insides are scattered on the floor in disarray.
I could get mad, not finding humor in this first-time play;
Or I could teach, let her touch, and let her learn
    from today.

March 5

It's your birthday! You're growing up so fast!
My baby of yesterday is a big boy at last.
Blow out your candles, may your wish come true.
Mine already has, another year with you.

October 28

On weekends, especially, there's one thing that's true,
As our children wake up, there's one thing they do.
It's as if a magnet is pulling each child
To our bed and bedroom; it gets sort of wild.

There's cuddling and hugging and rubbing of backs,
There's wiggling and giggling and tickling attacks.
But when it's all over, they scatter like mice,
Leaving a bed of destruction, but the silence is nice.

March 6

"Not now!" "Don't touch!" "Just go away!"
How often do you say these words each day?
"Okay!" "Let's Try!" "I love you so!"
Are much better words for your child to know.

October 27

In the beginning you're awake at night,
Rocking, feeding, and humming one song more.
Much later you're awake in the moonlight
Waiting for your teen's key in the door.

Sing and make music in your heart to the Lord, always giving thanks to God the Father for everything, in the name of our Lord Jesus Christ.

Ephesians 5:19,20

March 7

October 26

Just ask your child if a freshly raked pile
of crisp, crunchy, colorful fall leaves
is recyclable.

March 8

I stumble into the hot shower,
Breathe in the steam, let out a sigh.
The sound and force of the water
Sends my little worries good-bye.

I shampoo, singing a praise song,
And soak up the sun's first rays;
I step out refreshed and smiling,
Ready for God's brand new day.

Let your child *be* a child,
Finding joy in simple things.
Let him be silly, light, and funny;
Let his voice freely sing.

October 25

March 9

I rock in the stillness just before dawn,
Feeding, then watching your sweet little yawns.
I'm missing my sleep. I'm tired, that's true,
But this is my favorite time alone with you.

He will fill your mouth with laughter and your lips with shouts of joy.

Job 8:21

October 24

March 10

The spilled milk of yesterday is done.
Live today as if life has just begun.

When your child has had a very
    tough day,
Get off the phone, turn your
    friends away.

Find a place for just you two,
And eye-to-eye, let him share
    with you.

October 23

March 11

When a crocus pops through the last winter snow,
It's God's way of gently letting us know,
After a winter that's cold and dark,
Comes spring's hope and earth's new start.

When your world seems so dark and cold,
Remember the crocus and the Lord's words of old:
"I am with you always!" He has said;
He will give you hope, just ask to be led.

Lord, sharpen my mind
so I can see
The things that hurt You
in my child and me.
Lord, soften my heart so I can feel
Your love for me and know it's real.

October 22

March 12

When I'm angry, I should take the time
To sit down and count to nine.
Then pray for wisdom, peace, and grace
When I talk with my child face to face.

October 21

You can't wait 'til they crawl, but then...watch out!
You can't wait 'til they talk, but then...they shout!
You can't wait 'til they're grown and off on their own,
You can't wait for grandkids of your very own.

But don't wait! Enjoy today!
Savor each moment. It's more fun that way.

March 13

"In your anger do not sin": Do not let the sun go down while you are still angry.

Ephesians 4:26

October 20

Square roots, circumference,
You ask me to clarify.
Solids and molecules,
What temperature they liquify?

Helping you with questions
Is a challenge each night.
I want to encourage and guide,
But your homework I'll not write.

March 14

Lord, help me understand my child today;
Let me hear every word he may say.
Both words from his lips and those from his heart,
Being aware of his needs is a good place to start.

The sink backs up,
    the toilet overflows,
The washer breaks,
    the car needs a tow.

Once-in-awhile trials that
    give me a frown
Happen most often when my
    honey's out of town!

October 19

I love showering you with gifts,
I have time to read you a book.
You listen to all my stories,
You don't even care how I look.

I knew I would love you,
But I didn't have a clue,
Of what joy you'd bring my life,
And how my world now
    seems so new.

March 15

October 18

I love you too much to let you act this way.
I care for you too much to see a day thrown away.
Because of my love, I'll teach you right from wrong.
No matter what you do, this love is ever strong.

March 16

I buy the food and put it away!
I plan the meals and cook all day!
When the kitchen is clean and I collapse in a seat,
My children ask, "Is there anything to eat?"

October 17

Be kind and compassionate to one another,
forgiving each other, just as in Christ God forgave you.

Ephesians 4:32

March 17

Remember when the biggest decision in your life
was which china pattern to choose?
Children have a way of prioritizing priorities.

October 16

Control over your children should decrease
as their age and understanding increases.

A Blessing

Now to Him who is able to keep you from stumbling, and to make you stand in the presence of His glory blameless with great joy, to the only God our Savior, through Jesus Christ our Lord, be glory, majesty, dominion and authority, before all time and now and forever. Amen.

Jude 24,25

March 18

October 15

It's okay you made a mistake,
Mommy goofs up, too.
Just try again and do your best,
That's all I ask of you.

"Use an 'indoor voice'," I tend to say.
But, are they copying me when I yell that way?

October 14

My Doctor tells me to exercise more,
Like jogging, swimming, or buying a rope to skip.
But shouldn't he count running the stairs
Holding a child and a laundry basket on my hip?

Raindrops tapping at my
        window pane,
No thunder or lightning,
        just a light rain.
A day to slow down, yummy
        soup to cook;
And cuddle with my child
        reading piles of books.

March 20

October 13

Wash your hands with soap until they're clean.
Cover your mouth, then cough, there are germs unseen.
A mother is a teacher, nurse, and friend;
A child learns from her and on her depends.

March 21

Tiny tiptoes turn down the hall,
Many muffled giggles shared by all.
Seven slightly sleepy girls say,
"Can we sleep over again someday?"

If anyone serves, he should do it with the strength God provides, so that in all things God may be praised through Jesus Christ.

1 Peter 4:11

October 12

March 22

Did you know some bears give birth while in hibernation? When the mother bear awakens, her cubs are already walking, playing, and eating.

Though your child's first years may seem unbearable at times, don't be barely there and lose your bearings. Think of the joy the sleeping bear has missed. Wake up and enjoy your barefoot beauties.

I'm showered and dressed,
Ready to walk out the door;
You're fussy and crying,
You want me to hold you more.

Your nose is running, you're hot—
Why didn't I notice this before?
Lord, now what should I do?
Please open a new door.

October 11

I wish I could take this pain
   from you,
Your fever, cough, and
   congestion, too.

My heart aches to see you
   this way.
What else can I do?
   Sit down and pray.

March 23

October 10

"I hate wasting good food,"
   I always say.
So I save what's left and
   stash it away.

But what's behind that
   refrigerator door,
I don't mean to, but I
   tend to ignore.

Time goes by, then I pull out
   that dish;
"May I use that for science?"
   is now my son's wish.

Keep a camera on the counter
for catching those countless,
candid, cute keepsakes
of your cherub
or your clown.

March 24

October 9

I sat down my older children today
And told them they must listen to what I say:
No more threats or raising my voice,
I will ask once, and to obey is their choice.
If they say "no" or do not start to move,
There'll be consequences or fun privileges removed.

March 25

The memory of taking a home-made meal
to a sick friend, may last much longer than the
memorized words about love.

October 8

I have a drawer that's a total mess.
What's really there is anyone's guess:
Pencils, thumb tacks, rubberbands, too,
Legos®, gum, batteries, and glue.
To cleaning it out I'm not opposed,
But it's easier to forget it and keep it closed.

March 26

Share with God's people who are in need.
Practice hospitality.

Romans 12:13

October 7

Everyone should be quick to listen, slow to speak and slow to become angry.

James 1:19

March 27

You cried tonight.
You said I was unfair,
That I didn't understand,
You thought I didn't care.

But I do understand.
I was young, too.
I care so much,
That's why I'm protecting you.

But is protection what you need
At this time in your life?
Or freedom with love to discover
The joys *and* strife?

October 6

If I listen when she's young
And look her in the eye,
If I give her hugs and kisses
As each week flies by,

If I treat her with honesty,
And teach truths about You,
Then I'll be doing my best,
The best that I can do.

It's okay to give her a hug,
It's okay to miss her, too.
It's okay to say you love her,
For I love my good friend, too.

I know she's like a second mom,
Someone you're glad to see,
Someone you can talk to,
Someone who takes the
      place of me.

She's a gift to me and you,
A living angel from above,
Our lives are richer knowing her,
Let's thank her for her love.

March 28

October 5

With a tear of sadness but more smiles of joy
We took down the crib, our baby's a big boy.
Our big boy wants his own big bed,
New sheets and a pillow for his head.

No more lifting in or lifting him out,
Instead he just wants to jump and shout!
No bars and rails to keep him in,
Maybe he'll surprise me and, for once, sleep in.

March 29

I choose to read to my baby today,
She might not understand a thing I say.
But, just in case her little mind
Is begging to hear words of any kind...
I'll read and sing and talk all day,
'Til she talks to me in the very same way.

October 4

If there is one thing I want you to know,
It's that to strangers and even to friends,
It's okay to say NO!

March 30

Thank you for sitting so quietly today.
Thank you for putting your clothes away.
Thank you for staying calm when you wanted to yell.
Thank you for keeping that secret you wanted to tell.

Taking the time and remembering to praise,
Will bring you two closer and his confidence you'll raise.

October 3

I have them captive, they're buckled up.
Doors are locked, no one can interrupt.
It's the perfect time while in the van
To teach, sing, and listen to my clan.

March 31

A glass breaks! Then I hear them cry...
"She did it!" "No, he did it!" is their reply.
I didn't see it. Their word I must take.
My challenge...be fair, loving, and no favorites make.

October 2

At lunch when I can't be there,
A cookie-cuttered cheese heart says,
"I love you and I care."

April 1

Any time you think you have motherhood mastered,
reality returns.

October 1

Going the wrong way on a one-way street
   could cause pain.
So follow God's one-way life signs to remain
   happy and sane.

April 2

Help choose your toddler's tiny friends while you may,
For as a teen, peers help choose
What your child might do and say.

September 30

If any of you lacks wisdom, he should ask God, who gives generously to all without finding fault, and it will be given to him.

James 1:5

April 3

On those days when you don't have an extra
   ounce to give,
Take a short break and read His Book on how to live.
You'll feel renewed, your batteries He'll recharge
With energy and patience, so problems won't
   seem as large.

September 29

Wouldn't you know it, we're in a big store.
My "two" throws a tantrum. Where's the door?
A voice inside me says: "Be calm and pray.
Stop what you are doing, lead her away."

We walk to a corner. I hug her tight,
Review the rules: we'll not yell or fight.
Is she tired? Hungry? Wrong time of day?
Please give me wisdom for our next getaway.

April 4

"Come to me, all you who are weary and burdened, and I will give you rest."

Matthew 11:28

September 28

Some people get excited about
Climbing a mountain
Or sailing the open sea;
But seeing my son's face
As he rides his first bike
Is today's excitement for me.

April 5

Rocking gently, I sing her a song.
Rocking gently, she'll sleep
before long.
This song's the same she hears
me sing;
In no time at all she'll know the
same thing.

No matter how tired or busy
the day,
I repeat this ritual so someday
she'll pray,
The Lord's Prayer sung simply
from her heart.
What better gift can I give her
from the start?

September 27

No matter what grade your child receives on a test,
Make sure he knows he's your all-time best.

April 6

You read to your little sister,
You set the table and clean up, too,
You don't even complain too much
When you change a diaper or two.

You're sensitive and caring,
I can count on you to help me out.
I'm watching my boy become
    a man;
I'm so proud of you I could shout.

You may not appreciate it now,
This training I'm putting
    you through.
But someday, with children
    of your own,
As a Dad, you'll know what to do.

September 26

After having a baby I look in the mirror;
I see ripples, dimples, and layers, I fear.

My baby was worth it, no questioning that.
God used me for a miracle! This is "baby" fat.

Since it took nine months for my baby to grow,
I'll give myself the same for this weight to go!

April 7

When will there be time just for me.
To sit in quiet with a cup of tea?
Yet others say this phase isn't long.
Lord, help my blues turn to thankful song.

September 25

I want to hug your hurt away.
I want to heal you with my smile.
I want to make you feel much better,
Let's just cuddle a little while.

April 8

"I'm here, but tell her I'm not home!"
I instruct my daughter to answer the phone.
But what does my child *really* hear me say?
Since Mom lies...lying must be okay.

September 24

When I leave in the morning to be gone all day,
I picture you having fun at school or play.
But no matter where I am or whatever I do,
You're in my thoughts always. I sure love you!

April 9

Sitting together, still and silent,
   listening to the sounds of God's world
      may be that special gift you give your child today.

September 23

Whatever you do, work at it with all your heart, as though you were working for the Lord, and not for men. Remember the Lord will reward you.... For Christ is the real Master you serve.

Colossians 3:23-24 GNB

"Mommy, I need you!"
   "Mom, come see!"
My children pull at me
   so anxiously.

Two places at once, how can I be?
Help me be wise, sensitive, and
   choose carefully.

April 10

September 22

Do I expect perfection
From my children, husband and me?
Do I get upset
When things aren't just right I see?

Yet often my words speak the opposite,
Saying, "It's okay to make mistakes."
Lord, let me learn from my own words,
For myself, my husband's and children's sake.

A Blessing

May the God of peace, who through the blood of the eternal covenant brought back from the dead our Lord Jesus, that great Shepherd of the sheep, equip you with everything good for doing his will, and may he work in us what is pleasing to him, through Jesus Christ, to whom be glory for ever and ever.

Hebrews 13:20

April 11

September 21

We may disagree, but feel free to speak.
Tell me the full story, no matter how bleak.
I'll love you forever, no matter what you do.
There may be consequences, but I'll stand by you.

April 12

One of the biggest challenges of potty training
is training the mom not to forget.

September 20

It's date night, so where do we go?
To the video store to rent a good show.
The evening is planned, we cannot wait,
Then our daughter gets sick from something she ate.

Our son cries since his sister is sad,
So I cuddle our daughter, our son's with Dad.
Now it's after ten, do we start the show
Or return it unwatched? Where did date night go?

I gave my child two things
    of her own,
To unlock the doors of places
    unknown.

Choosing from things of the world
    was hard,
But I gave her a Bible and
    a library card.

April 13

September 19

A child remembers what he hears and sees.
He memorizes stories, a new song's a breeze.

What else does he remember from a day with you...
Phone talk, your music, TV commercials, too?

Though an imprint on the sand may wash away,
An imprint on a young mind may be there to stay.

April 14

I get on my knees to wipe up a spill,
Then on pops a rider for a pony-ride thrill.
I'm not too happy about the mess today,
But I can change my mood and take a moment to play.

September 18

The first cute smile. The first real crawl.
The first new bike. The first bad fall.
A first can be fun if it leaves no scar,
But what about the first time our teen drives our car?

April 15

Six active gifts to give your child:
Time, touching, and talking
Listening, laughing, and loving.

A Blessing

May the God of hope fill you with all joy and peace as you trust in him, so that you may overflow with hope by the power of the Holy Spirit.

Romans 15:13

September 17

April 16

Sometimes when I'm in the pit of despair,
I wonder if you're listening and really there.
Will you turn my sorrow into something good?
Will I sing your praises where sadness stood?
Then I pray, remembering your promises to me,
And in time maybe your plan for me I'll see.

A new school year, there's so
    much to do,
With forms, fund raisers,
    activities, too.

Yet, find the time to pray
    for each teacher.
Write a note of thanks,
    your love will reach her.

September 16

April 17

So do not throw away your confidence; it will be richly rewarded. You need to persevere so that when you have done the will of God, you will receive what he has promised.

Hebrews 10:35,36

As our children grow before
    our eyes,
We need to loosen our love ties.

September 15

April 18

We teach our children not to call each other names,
But when we use our child's cute nickname,
   might we be doing the same?

September 14

No matter how much you think you remember
how a newborn will alter your life, when it happens
it's obvious you've forgotten.

April 19

For a child's trust in you to grow and bloom,
water it with honesty, feed it with consistency,
and shine on it the bright light of unconditional love,
even when darkness surrounds it.

September 13

Correcting homework
Or evaluating a job that's done,
First find the good points
And praise each, one by one.

Then lovingly share
What needs improvement still,
Downplaying his mistakes,
Reaffirming existing skills.

April 20

Dishes are piled, beds aren't made,
But my child wants me to go out and play.
Lord, remind me gently that dishes and beds can wait,
For in no time at all, my child will be on her way.

Recycle your children's artwork—
Encourage them to do more.

The most meaningful card
   to Grandma
May come off your
   refrigerator door.

September 12

April 21

I have to capture it all, she's growing so fast.
I want to remember each moment and make
the memories last.

Looking at my pictures, there's nothing I lack,
Looking at my checkbook, I should own Fuji or Kodak!

Whatever is true,
    whatever is noble,
Whatever is right,
    whatever is pure,
Whatever is lovely,
    whatever is admirable—
If anything is excellent
    or praiseworthy—
Think about such things.

Philippians 4:8

September 11

"Turn off the lights!"
"Don't let the water run."
"Don't throw that away,
We'll recycle every one."

"Conserve," "Recycle"
Are the words of today.
But it's Mom who
   orchestrates
The efforts each day.

April 22

September 10

When Daddy's not home, whether at work or play,
I could talk about him in a negative way.
But I need to be positive in the words I say
So their love-bond will strengthen even when he's away.

I want to be my child's friend,
But also a teacher and one
    to defend.
I want to encourage, love,
    and praise.
Thank you for this child you've
    given me to raise.

April 23

September 9

Just as I'm ready to make my bed,
My child jumps in and covers her head.
Now there's a lump that moves and giggles.
I might as well join her and hug out those wiggles.

April 24

Give thanks to the Lord, for he is good;
his love endures forever.

Psalm 107:1

On that first day of school
As I walked you to the bus
You were excited and giggly,
You didn't want me to fuss.

As you climbed up the steps
You glanced back with fear,
So I smiled, blew you a kiss,
Turned and wiped away my tear.

September 8

April 25

Sometimes in my hurry
With my list of things to do,
I forget to stop and listen
To these important words from you:
"See my picture?" "Smell my flower."
"Please read a book to me."
So, I'll slow down and take the time,
Because you're my love, my priority.

September 7

Pick out a Bible verse from the "breakfast bin,"
Read it, say grace—it's a good way to begin.

April 26

Teachers come in all sizes.
To learn from a child, swallow your pride,
    open your ears, close your mouth,
    and listen from your heart.

September 6

My loved one is gone,
I'll never forget that day.
Yet others get busy,
And let it pass away.

Today is for memories.
Tomorrow I may mourn.
But I smile with thanksgiving,
Thinking of the day he was born.

April 27

When your child is grown and gone
And expresses his free will,
Remember you did the best you could,
You loved him and always will.

September 5

Letting go
And letting your child try something for the first time
Is hard to do,
For you could do it yourself and save some valuable time.

He needs to try,
And it may take some spills before he finally gets it right.
Find the good
And always keep your long-term goal in sight.

April 28

My child,

Notice the beauty of the world out there;
Notice the love and those who share;
Notice what you give and not what you get;
Notice the new student is a friend you haven't met.

September 4

Learn to put aside your own desires so that you will become patient and godly, gladly letting God have his way with you.

2 Peter 1:6 TLB

April 29

One of the smallest parts of our body
    can cause the most damage to the spirit of our child...
        our tongue.

At "two," the ME in each of us
　　　is at it's peak,
MY wants, MY needs, is all a "two"
　　　wants to seek.

As we grow and we're aware
　　　of others in our life,
The ME still appears, especially
　　　in times of strife.

But now as a mom, it's my child's
　　　needs I willingly meet,
God has replaced the big ME
　　　with His love so sweet.

September 3

April 30

The tongue is a small thing, but what enormous damage it can do.

James 3:5 TLB

"Kick the ball!" "Get up!"
"NO...run the OTHER way!"
Parents yell excitedly
On soccer's opening day.

My daughter falls and cries,
She got kicked in the knee.
A coach lovingly picks her up,
And carries her to me.

September 2

May 1

A hand-picked spring flower bouquet
Is a gift of love to brighten your day.

September 1

But Mom,
don't get depressed thinking about getting older;
think of it as one day closer to being with Jesus
where with Him you will be young forever.

:   :

May 2

Who has the most influence
On what your child might hear and see?
Is it you, teachers, peers...
Or that ever-present TV?

August 31

Be completely humble and gentle;
be patient, bearing one another in love.

Ephesians 4:2

May 3

A mom is also a child of God.
He will protect, lead, and nurture us, too,
if we just let Him in and ask Him to.

I try to keep myself in shape;
I try to tune in to what is "cool."
Yet, now I've noticed something
That's not the exception,
    but the rule.

"Mom, can I wear your shirt?"
"Your jeans fit me just fine."
My teen likes my taste and size,
But are my clothes hers or mine?

August 30

May 4

Sometimes I'm tempted to wish I were someone I'm not.
Sometimes I'm envious of others outwardly or in thought.
Sometimes I don't feel the contentment I should.
Lord, help me to give thanks, for all You make is good.

It's amazing how much
   grandmothers know
      about raising children...
Just ask, then truly listen.

August 29

Wouldn't it be nice if a mother's kiss and a Snoopy™ bandaid could cure all of our children's hurts?

May 5

August 28

A summer sunset sky,
Of pink, purple, and blue
Reminds me
That each day is a work of art
Created for me by You.

Be joyful in hope, patient in affliction, faithful in prayer.

Romans 12:12

May 6

August 27

The house is quiet. The bedrooms stay neat.
I'm making dinner for only two of us to eat.
There's college, jobs or places of their own,
And I'm anxiously awaiting our talks on the phone.

But on the weekends and holidays, guess who's
    at our door...
Borrowing the car, talking on the phone,
Bags of laundry on the floor?

May 7

Praying with your child
Need not be solemn or hushed.
Praying with your child
Need not be memorized or rushed.

Pray with your child,
From your heart, simple and direct;
Your child will learn from you,
And God's love he'll not reject.

August 26

Our children are yours, mine, and ours,
but first of all HIS.

Balance every "no" with seven "yes's," and you will find
A more peaceful home and a child who wants to mind.

May 8

Lord, give me insight to know
my baby's needs,
Give me wisdom to know
right and wrong.

Give me strength to make it
through the day,
Give me a thankful heart all
day long.

August 25

May 9

Give yourself a big pat on the back,
Say, "I'm doing my best, no matter what I lack."
God's your main boss, and He likes what you do,
For you're raising the gifts He's given to you.

A Blessing

May the Lord answer you when you are in distress; may the name of the God of Jacob protect you. May he send you help and grant you support.... May he give you the desire of your heart and make all your plans succeed.... May the Lord grant all your requests.

Psalm 20:1,2,4,5

August 24

May 10

You are special!
Find time to discover you.
You are unique!
Your gifts are designed for you.
You are a woman,
Daughter and mother, too.
Find the joy,
In whatever you choose to do.

August 23

There are instructions for most everything you buy.
There are warranties if they break and go awry.
But where's the guide for this child you've given me?
Is the Bible and Your love, an unconditional warranty?

Blessed is the [mother] who fears the Lord, who finds great delight in his commands. [Her] children will be mighty in the land; the generation of the upright will be blessed.

Even in darkness light dawns for the upright, for the gracious and compassionate and righteous [woman]. Surely [she] will never be shaken; a righteous [mother] will be remembered forever.

May 11

Psalm 112:1,2,3,4,6 (adapted)

August 22

"Touch it once,"
  I always say,
As I teach my child to
  put things away.

"Let it not find a place
  to rest
Until you have found
  the place that's best."

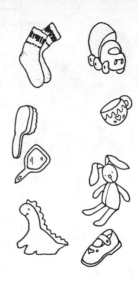

May 12

Your child is your legacy.
Don't let a generation yet to come
    wish you had never begun.

August 21

Let your child grow and try what he can;
Encourage him with words and a helping hand.
Don't keep him sheltered from trying what he must,
Just be near by, so in you he can trust.

May 13

Sometimes when I'm down,
My kids give my spirits a lift.
Then there are other times,
I need Your patience to endure
    my little gifts.

August 20

When you feel alone and down,
You deserve a lift, that's true.
Call another mom in town
Who understands what you're going through.

May 14

Nursing mothers are an endangered race,
Forgot about often when it's restrooms we face.
We sit on the sink, on the pot if we must...
Or on the floor in the corner with the cobwebs and dust.

All we need is a couch, a wooden chair would do
To nurse our babies and change them, too.
But my baby doesn't care, so why should I?
Yet, if I can change it, I'm sure going to try.

August 19

It's surprising how a teenage girl will share it all
During a quiet lunch and a walk through a mall.

A teenager's bedroom is his safety zone from the outside world.

The challenge is keeping it from being a danger zone to walk through.

May 15

Give him a hug. Say you're sorry.
Your brother is your best friend!
For in time you will see,
On each other you will depend.

August 18

May 16

When I'm frazzled and tired,
It's so hard to see
Wisdom in handling Your child
Whom You've entrusted to me.

Help me find rest,
And a quiet moment or two;
Please direct my thoughts
To focus only on You.

As believers in our glorious Lord Jesus Christ, don't show favoritism. "Love your neighbor as yourself."

James 2:1,8

May 17

The wisdom that comes from heaven is first of all pure; then peace loving, considerate, submissive, full of mercy and good fruit, impartial and sincere.

James 3:17

August 16

One of your children may be just like you,
Thinking, acting, and feeling as you do.
Another may be your opposite in many ways,
Causing numerous challenging and frustrating days.

Yet, we are asked to give love and be fair
To each equally and show we care.
We can't take sides or favorites choose,
For in the process, a child's spirit we'll lose.

May 18

Love them, pray for them, try your best each day.
Forgive them, play with them, teach them God's Way.
When they get older and ask questions of you,
You can honestly say, "I did the best I could do."

August 15

I have been wronged
By someone I call my friend.
Lord, help me forgive, show love,
And friendship still extend.

May 19

Start today! Please don't wait!
Pray for your child's future mate.

August 14

Why is it over summer vacation
my child's reasoning skills
also take a summer break?

Walk in your child's shoes today.
See what he sees, feel what he feels.
Then you may come to really know
His hurts, concerns, and joys
    are real.

May 20

August 13

That's too bad you lost today,
But say, "Good job!" to your sister who won.
Next time you may be the winner,
So play again, and together have fun.

May 21

There's plenty of time to be grown-up.
It's your child's turn to be young.
Take the weight from her tiny shoulders,
Lighten up, Mom, quiet your tongue.

August 12

Turn off the TV.
Pull out the lawn chair.
Sit under the stars.
Breathe in the night air.

Listen to the night sounds,
See a falling star or two.
God doesn't make reruns.
Each night is brand new.

May 22

It's been a long day! All the kids are in bed.
Prayers have been prayed, books have been read.
I need a moment just for me,
To put up my feet and sip my tea.
The moment will be fleeting, for in no time at all
I'll hear the crumpled clothes of the laundry call.

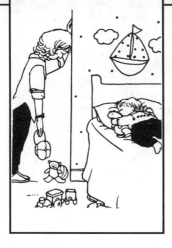

Sometimes a child doesn't
   need a nap
As much as a mother needs
   a break.

August 11

May 23

I see other mothers teach their children
In ways that are quite different from me.
Lord, help me not to judge or be envious.
Help me be the best that I can be.

He took the children in his arms, put his hands on them and blessed them.

Mark 10:16

August 10

Let us not become conceited, provoking and envying each other.

Galatians 5:26

May 24

August 9

Universal signs of love to any child...
a gentle touch, a warm hug, a sincere kiss,
and a night-time backrub.

May 25

Unless the outfit is indecent,
Or in extremely poor taste,
Let it be...
Or it's precious time you'll waste.

August 8

Often I look for shortcuts
In the things I choose to do.
But there is no shortcut I will find
When I'm quietly listening to you.

May 26

My child, I love you no matter what you do,
where you go, or how you feel about me.
I love you no matter what!

August 7

I'm feeling so tired, no energy, no pep.
I don't want to get up or take one step.
I have my crackers on the table by my bed,
Yet, the thought of food is something I dread.

But I need to eat, to help my baby grow,
To have energy for my others who still need me, I know.
The thought of my sweethearts makes me sit up tall,
Then slowly take slippered steps down the hall.

To the kitchen I'm going, which is not my favorite sight,
I've got to think more positively and set my attitude right.
I will eat good food, and I'll try to keep it down,
The trimester's soon over; come on smiles, goodbye frowns.

May 27

Today find the fun in whatever you do,
For tomorrow there's another pile of laundry to do.

August 6

"Are we there yet?" is the traveling cry.
"Are we there yet?" I take a deep sigh.
"Are we there yet?" The time passes so slow.
Are vacations worth the effort?
When we get there, I'll let you know.

May 28

I don't expect perfection,
You don't have to get all A's.
You don't have to win awards,
Or be a scholar and amaze.

I want you to be just you,
And forget about the rest.
Take your time, give it a try;
And do your personal best!

Be joyful always; pray continually; give thanks in all circumstances, for this is God's will for you in Christ Jesus.

1 Thessalonians 5:16-18

August 5

May 29

My husband and I
Don't always "parent" the same.
We come from different backgrounds,
It's not him I should blame.

God made us unique,
With different gifts to use.
I need to appreciate his insight,
Or his input I may lose.

August 4

Thank you for my children;
They are such gifts to me.
Thank you for their laughs and giggles,
Through their eyes I clearly see.

Thank you for their little fights,
It gives me a chance to teach.
Even thanks for their fears and hurts,
Then it is You to whom I reach.

May 30

Every soldier who dies for freedom
is a mother's child. Let's not take for granted
our freedom for which they died.

August 3

You two can disagree
And state respectfully what you think.
But remember your brother is your friend,
And forever you'll have that love link.

May 31

To all who mourn...he will give:
    Beauty for ashes;
    Joy instead of mourning;
    Praise instead of heaviness.
For God has planted them like strong and
graceful oaks for his own glory.

Isaiah 61:3 TLB

August 2

Listen to what your child says...
Not to what you think he may say.

June 1

I wish you could talk and tell me
    how to give you comfort from
    crying now.
I fed you, hugged you, and know
    you're dry. Are you hot? Too
    cold? Please don't cry.

What should I do? Should I sing
    you a song? I pray you'll sleep
    before very long.

Ah...you're asleep, how peaceful
    you look. I should put you
    down, I have dinner to cook.
But nothing else matters when I
    see you rest, 'Cause now is the
    time I love the best.

I'm standing in line at the
   grocery store
With no children in my arms
   or cart.

Yet, I still find myself
   gently swaying;
Though alone, I still rock them
   in my heart.

August 1

June 2

To really love your teenager,
   set her boundaries with love,
      allow her room to grow,
         and when it's time, let her go.

July 31

When you're tired, exhausted,
Feeling no one seems to care,
Get on your knees and cry to Him.
He's listening and is always there.

To my child who cries for no apparent reason,
I want to say, "Stop it! Don't feel that way!"
But I catch myself just in time and say,
"I'm here...tell me why you feel that way."

July 30

Let your gentleness be evident to all.
Philippians 4:5

June 4

When I see my daughter pretending to be me,
It doesn't seem long ago I wondered what I'd be.
I made many choices, some good, others bad.
But You were there for me, and for that I'm so glad.
I need to encourage my child and keep all
    my motives pure,
Seeking both Your will in her life and the gifts
    You've given her.

July 29

If I want my child to be
    caring, gentle, and kind,
      considerate of others he may reach,
I need to be an example
    and take the time,
      to lovingly guide and teach.

June 5

Encourage the timid, help the weak, be patient with everyone.

1 Thessalonians 5:14

July 28

When God made the motor for toddlers,
There's one thing He forgot, I fear.
Often, the throttle gets stuck on high,
For He forgot to include low gear!

June 6

Mom, if you make me feel stupid and small,
I won't have any confidence at all.
Praise and encourage me and see me grow;
My spirit and esteem will be aglow.

July 27

Often a child's creativity appears
    when the TV and scheduled activities disappear.

June 7

As simple as taking the time
To admire a child's catch of the day
Might be today's key
For keeping his ears open to what you say.

A child's crisis is very real to him.
Listen to his heart as well as
 his words.
Don't turn his mountain into a
 molehill.
When you listen and understand
 from his level,
He will walk down his mountain
 to safe ground.

July 26

June 8

A child grows best in a climate
of love, acceptance, joy, and peace.

July 25

Two's and teens are similar...
They both need:

Boundaries with flexible fences,
Your time and tender love,
Persistency and consistency,
And all His help from above.

There are toys for grownups,
There are toys for a child.
You could spend money daily
And really go wild.

But what do you feel
When the excitement is gone?
Are you sad, depressed,
Bored and withdrawn?

...continued

June 9

Clothe yourselves with compassion, kindness, humility, gentleness and patience.

Colossians 3:12

July 24

June 10

Instead...
Help those who are lonely, care for a child who is sick.
Help build a home for the homeless out of love
    and some bricks.
Share your gifts with others less fortunate than you,
And you'll feel God's blessings laid gently on you.

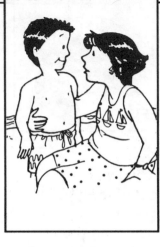

If a child seems deaf to what you
   may say, look at the message in
   your words today.
Do you correct and order him
   about? Do you talk above,
   beneath; do you shout?

Sit down together face-to-face;
   ask forgiveness for being
   "on his case."
Listen, ask questions, show gentle
   care; His ears will open, ask
   Jesus in prayer.

July 23

The world and its desires pass away, but the man who does the will of God lives forever.

1 John 2:17

June 11

July 22

Selling lemonade in the hot summer sun
To friends passing by can be so much fun.
I remember doing this same summer thing,
I'd sit for hours, in the quiet I'd sing.
Some childhood memories are re-created for me,
While watching my child enjoy life carefree.

June 12

With tears of gladness, I celebrate this day!
With tears of sadness, he'll soon be on his way.
With tears of pride, I've helped a boy become a man;
With tears of release, Lord, he's now in Your hand.

July 21

Isn't it funny how as a little girl
I couldn't wait to put on my mom's high heels,
But as a grownup I can't wait to take them off?

June 13

Grandparents have a special way
Of taking time from their busy day
To play a game or take a walk,
To snuggle quietly or just talk.

They're not in the hurry I see in myself.
They're not always looking at the clock on the shelf.
Thank You for grandparents, let me learn from them still
How to slow down, enjoy, and follow Your will.

July 20

Peanut butter on the counter top,
Strawberry jam dripping to the floor.
I teach my teen to take care of himself,
But at clean-up time, he's out the door.

June 14

Mom, don't tell me what to wear!
Mom, please help me with my hair.
Mom, let me do it and work it through!
Mom, help...please tell me what to do.
Mom, don't touch me, you're in my way.
Mom, I really need your hug today.

One minute it's "Yes!" the next it's "No!"
This, too, will pass; that's how teens grow.

If television is on in your home does it...

Teach?...
Enlighten?
Lift spirits?...
Entertain wholesomely?
Vitalize?...
Inspire?...
Soothe?
Illuminate?...
Offer options?
Nudge when necessary?

July 19

June 15

It seems like yesterday
You were my baby,
My precious little one.
And yet, now you're grown;
Life with your husband
Has just begun.

...continued

July 18

Discipline your son, and he will give you peace;
he will bring delight to your soul.

Proverbs 29:17

June 16

I pray for love and laughter,
And ears that listen first, before you speak.
I pray for compromise and compassion,
And that Jesus you both shall seek.

...continued

July 17

Do you want the blue or green one?
Do you want to go outside and play?
Asking your child's opinion
Has it's proper place each day.
But when it gets out of balance
And your *child* is in control,
It's time to teach and tell with love
And regain your parental role.

June 17

I pray for health and harmony,
That the other's happiness you seek most.
I pray you'll learn to forget and forgive;
Focus on his strengths for which you can boast.

...continued

July 16

Each day is a series of special moments,
Some hidden, others so clear.
Discover and treasure these moments
And hold those you love so near.

June 18

I pray you'll remember I'm your friend,
And I'll always be here for you...
To cry to or laugh with and to
Share your dreams and doubts with, too.

...continued

Vacations can be fun,
But it's tiring just preparing
for one....

What to bring? What still to do?
What to wash? What to buy new?
What to pack? What to save for
the road?

I need a vacation from planning
this vacation
Or I might just explode!

July 15

And then, in time,
When you're a mom
With children of your own,
I pray you'll feel as I do...
Your children are His gift on loan.

June 19

July 14

Sometimes their music may be too loud in your ears.
Sometimes their clothes may make you want to laugh
   to tears.
Sometimes their slang words may seem a little strange.
Think back to when you were a teen—your outlook
   may change.

It takes effort to be consistent.
It's much easier to just ignore.
But consistency pays off—
Reap the benefits when he's four.

June 20

July 13

No matter how frustrated and angry you may be,
Don't say, "I'll leave you if you don't come now with me!"
You know you wouldn't do it. You know that it's not true.
Think of a better solution that works for both of you.

June 21

Your investment of focused, unhurried time today
will yield a return beyond your greatest expectations.

July 12

But God's truth stands firm like a great rock,
and nothing can shake it.

2 Timothy 2:19 TLB

June 22

I can't always stop him when he wants to go.
I can't always stand by him and help him say "no".
I can't always be there in his time of need,
But I can teach him Your Word, and that You'll intercede.

July 11

As the waves wash away
My child's castle made of sand,
It reminds me that our foundation
Should be laid by God's Word and hand.

June 23

My son, if sinners entice you, do not give in to them.
My son, do not go along with them, do not set foot
on their paths.

Proverbs 1:10,15

July 10

My child fell today, but hardly a scratch I see.
Yet, by her tears you would think she'd broken her knee.
I want to say, "Stop crying, it's not really that bad!"
But compassion wins, "I bet it hurts, no wonder
    you're sad."
I change the subject and show her something else to play,
And in no time at all, the hurt has gone away.

Before my children go to school
   or play,
I'd like to get a can of Scotch-gard®
   spray.
Wouldn't it be nice if I could spray
   them all
To protect them from bullies, bad
   words, and falls?
Since I can't, there's only one thing
   to say,
"Lord, please protect and guard
   them along their way."

June 24

July 9

They say I radiate, and I guess I do.
     I feel good; I'm excited just
        waiting for you.
A feeling of expectancy, never
     realized what that meant...
Like, "waiting impatiently" for the
     miracle God has sent.

I feel like I'm special, and God has
     chosen me
To nurture His creation before
     everyone gets to see...
His work of art that's taking only
     nine months to create;
He's using me daily, I guess that's
     why I radiate.

June 25

Saying "no" to a good friend
Is hard for my child to do
When they get into mischief
Or want to try something new.

I must develop his conscience
So he can make good decisions alone.
Please give me wisdom and direction
To guide your gift given to me on loan.

July 8

Lord, I want my home to be
Peaceful, joyful, a place to worship You.
I want my home to have
Open doors to my children and their friends, too.
I want my home to remain
A place of love where children can express
Their worries, hurts, joys, and loves,
A home of acceptance and happiness.

June 26

I can quiet your cries, I can soothe your brow
By holding and feeding you as I'm doing now.
We're creating a bond, just you and I,
That God will strengthen as time passes by.

I praise you because I am fearfully and wonderfully made; your works are wonderful, I know that full well.

Psalm 139:14

July 7

June 27

A wise mom knows when to pull in the reins
and when to let them go.

July 6

Sometimes, I look in the mirror and see things
    I'd like to change or slightly rearrange.
But then I think of God's handiwork in a snowflake
    or a flower, and babies born each hour.
He has purpose and design with each created babe.
    I'll stay as I am, for I was custom-made.

June 28

It's summertime!
School is finally out!
The countdown has ended,
You can hear the kids shout!

I'm excited, too,
But I'm much more discreet.
No more carpools and activities,
I can get off the street!

July 5

I look back to when I said, "I do."
My dreams, my hopes were all
    so new.
Candlelight dinners, surprises just
    for him,
Wearing make-up, keeping fit at
    the gym.

But now my children take my
    energy and time,
Working, dinner, laundry—I'm
    exhausted at bedtime.
I need to prioritize, for I would not
    want to lose
My husband, our love; Lord, help
    me wisely choose.

A Blessing

The Lord bless you, and keep you;
The Lord make His face shine on
you and be gracious on you;
The Lord lift up His countenance
on you, and give you peace.

Numbers 6:24-26 NAS

June 29

July 4

Let freedom ring from inner cities to mountains high.
Let freedom ring from pastures to towers that touch
the sky.

Let freedom ring from the East all the way to the West.
Let freedom ring through this land we love the best.

Let freedom ring from my words and actions others see.
Let freedom ring daily, for it's God's desire and decree.

June 30

Just because other moms say it's okay
Doesn't mean it's right or it's our way.

July 3

When we take them only to the extraordinary,
The spectacular—the amazing, too—
Our children can lose the awe
Of simple creations designed by You.

July 1

My child is so busy exploring her world that's new.
Wanting to touch, taste, see, and smell,
And climb on a table or two.
I need to be creative when controlling her new zeal,
And be careful not to crush her desire to learn what's real.

Yet, I need to set limits and teach her how to mind.
But I'll save the strong NO's for the important and
    unsafe I find.

July 2

What's better than
frolicking family fun in a crisp,
clear country lake at vacation time?